FOOD SCIENCE

INSTRUCTIONS

1 Open the front flap on the VR viewer. Bring the top and side flaps up and over. The side flaps attach to the side of the viewer with Velcro.

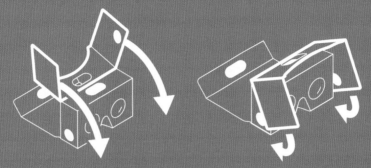

2 Download PI VR Food, available on the App Store or Google Play. Direct links to the store locations are found at: pilbooks.com/PIVRFood.

3 Launch the app. You may be asked to calibrate your viewer by scanning the QR code found on the bottom of the viewer itself. You will be able to change your viewer settings later in the options menu.

4 After calibrating your viewer, you will be prompted to scan the QR code found to the right to verify your possession of this book.

5 You will see a double image of a farm on your phone. Insert your smartphone into the front compartment of the VR viewer. The line between the two images should line up with the notch at the center point of the viewer, between the two lenses. If your screen seems blurry, make sure the smartphone is aligned precisely with the center of the viewer. Adjusting the phone left or right a few millimeters can make a big difference. The tilt of the viewer and the phone can also affect how the screen looks to you.

6 Look around to explore! PI VR Food does not require a lever or remote control. You control each interaction with your gaze. When you see a loading circle, keep your gaze focused until it loads fully to access videos, slideshows, and games.

Loading

7 Gaze at the X to close out of video, slideshow, or game screens.

Exit

Publications International, Ltd.

Get the App!

This book is enhanced by an app that can be downloaded from the App Store or Google Play*. Apps are available to download at no cost. Once you've downloaded the app to your smartphone**, use the QR code found on page 1 of this book to access an immersive, 360˚ virtual reality environment. Then slide the phone into the VR viewer and you're ready to go.

Compatible Operating Systems

- Android 4.1 (JellyBean) or later

- iOS 8.0 or later

Compatible Phones

The app is designed to work with smartphones with a screen size of up to 6 inches. Removing your device from its case may provide a better fit in the viewer. If your smartphone meets the above operating system requirements and has gyroscope functionality it should support GoogleVR. Publications International, Ltd. has developed and tested this software with the following devices:

- Google Nexus 5, Google Nexus 5X

- Motorola Moto Z

- Apple iPhone 6, Apple iPhone 6 Plus, Apple iPhone 7, Apple iPhone 8, Apple iPhone X

- Samsung Galaxy S6, Samsung Galaxy S6 Edge, Samsung Galaxy S7, Samsung Galaxy S8

Caution

The viewer should not be exposed to moisture or extreme temperatures. The viewer is not water resistant. It is potentially combustible if the lenses are left facing a strong light source.

Apple, the Apple logo and iPhone are trademarks of Apple Inc., registered in the U.S. and other countries. App Store is a service mark of Apple Inc., registered in the U.S. and other countries. Google Play and the Google Play logo are trademarks of Google Inc. Nexus is a trademark of Google Inc. Samsung and Galaxy are trademarks of Samsung Electronics Co. Ltd. MOTOROLA and the Stylized M logo are registered trademarks of Motorola Trademark Holding, LLC.

 Publications International, Ltd.

For inquiries email: customer_service@pubint.com

ISBN: 978-1-64030-330-0

Manufactured in China.

8 7 6 5 4 3 2 1

*We reserve the right to terminate the apps.
**Smartphone not included. Standard data rates may apply to download. Once downloaded, the app does not use data or require Wi-Fi access.

CONTENTS

Introduction 4

The Food Chain 6

Food and Nutrition 8

Agriculture 12

The Development of Farming 14

Domestication 16

Modern Farms 18

Farming Methods Around the World 22

Agricultural Fairs 24

Farm Machinery 26

Irrigation 30

Soil Conservation 32

Pest Control 34

Corn 36

Wheat 37

Rice 38

Potatoes 39

Orchards 40

Cattle 42

Milk 44

Sheep 46

Goats 47

Poultry 48

Pigs 50

The Meat Industry 52

Aquaculture 54

Sugar 56

Chocolate 57

Food Preservation 58

Test What You Know 60

INTRODUCTION

Plants make their own food with the Sun's help. Animals, including humans, do not. Instead they eat food—plants or other animals—to get what their bodies need to live and grow. Nutrition is the science of how the body uses food.

CALORIES

Food gives the body the energy it needs for everything it does, from repairing damaged cells to sleeping. The amount of energy a food can produce is measured in calories. When a person eats more food than the body needs, the body changes the extra calories into fat. Eating fewer calories than the body needs will cause a person to lose weight.

The number of calories needed by people each day depends on how much energy their bodies use. For example, an athlete usually needs more calories than an adult who works at a desk all day.

Exercise helps people burn calories.

EATING HEALTHY

Different foods contain different combinations of nutrients. Some foods are better sources of nutrients than others. Scientists have created charts and pictures to show how much a person should eat from different food groups in order to be healthy.

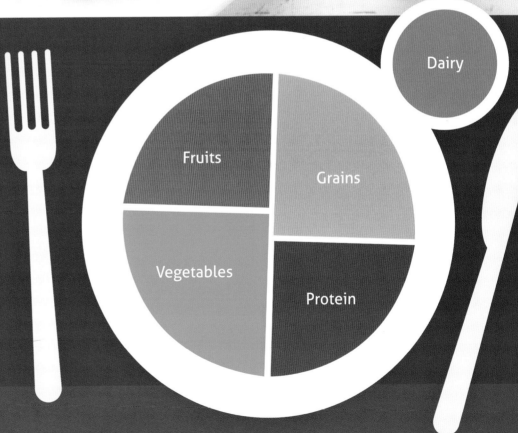

USE THE VR VIEWER AND ASSOCIATED APP

Enhance your experience by using the app! Put your smartphone in the VR viewer and you'll be able to explore a farm. See a video, play a game, and more!

THE FOOD CHAIN

The term *food chain* refers to a series of linked feeding relationships between living things in an ecosystem. More specifically, a food chain describes the order in which matter and energy in the form of food are transferred from one organism to another. Because most organisms eat more than one type of plant or animal, an organism may belong to more than one food chain. As a result, the food chains in an ecosystem overlap and intertwine to form a complex food web.

TROPHIC LEVELS

Food chains are organized across several trophic, or feeding, levels. Organisms at each level feed on organisms from the level below and are in turn eaten by organisms from the level above. A typical grassland food chain would extend from grasses to rabbits (which eat grasses), to snakes (which eat rabbits), and to hawks (which eat snakes).

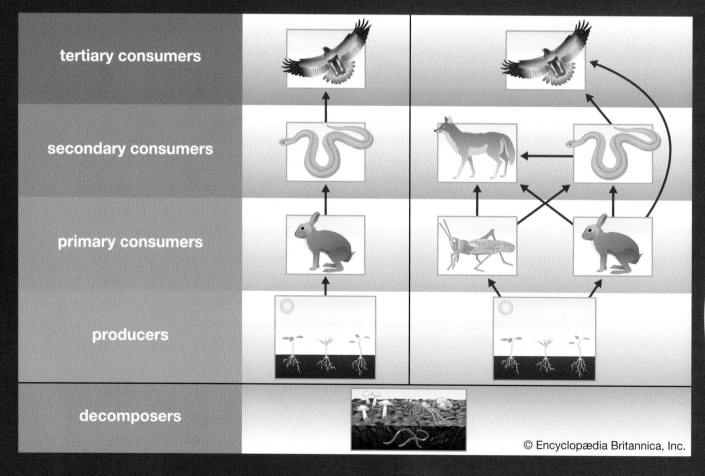

tertiary consumers

secondary consumers

primary consumers

producers

decomposers

© Encyclopædia Britannica, Inc.

A food chain (left) shows how matter and energy from food are transferred from one organism to another. In a natural ecosystem, many food chains intertwine to form a complex food web (right).

PRODUCERS

Organisms at the first level in a food chain are called producers. These are organisms that can make their own food. They use photosynthesis to convert light energy from the Sun into the chemical energy of food.

Deer and rabbits are both primary consumers.

A buzzard searches for prey.

CONSUMERS

Organisms in the remaining trophic levels are called consumers. The organisms at the second level of the food chain are called primary consumers. These are organisms that eat producers. The third level of the food chain contains secondary consumers. These are animals that eat primary consumers. Many food chains have a fourth level that contains tertiary consumers—animals that eat secondary consumers. Some very large ecosystems may have a fifth level that consists of quaternary consumers. These are animals that eat tertiary consumers and, in some cases, secondary and even primary consumers.

Foods rich in carbohydrates.

FOOD AND NUTRITION

Food provides essential substances called nutrients. The body needs these nutrients to help it make energy; to grow, repair, and maintain its tissues; and to keep its different systems working smoothly. Nutrition is important for all organisms—including humans.

KINDS OF NUTRIENTS

Nutrients are divided into six major types: carbohydrates, proteins, fats, vitamins, minerals, and water. Each nutrient performs specific functions to keep the body healthy. All the nutrients work together to contribute to good health.

CARBOHYDRATES

The body's main source of energy is carbohydrates, which include starches and sugars, and dietary fiber. The body breaks down and converts starches and sugars into the simple sugar glucose, the main energy source for all the cells of the body.

Starches are complex carbohydrates. They are found in dry beans and peas, such as kidney beans, pinto beans, soybeans, chickpeas, lentils, and split peas; grains and grain products, such as breads and cereals; potatoes; and other vegetables.

Sugars, or simple carbohydrates, also are a natural part of many foods.

Dietary fiber provides neither energy nor essential nutrients. Fiber is the structural part of plants, and the human body cannot digest it. However, eating dietary fiber is beneficial to the body in many ways. Fiber aids digestive health and may protect against certain disorders and diseases.

Foods rich in protein.

PROTEINS

Proteins are made of amino acids, small units necessary for growth and tissue repair. About one-fifth of the body's total weight is protein. Hair, skin, muscles, internal organs, and bones are made primarily of protein.

FATS

Fats are a concentrated source of energy (having more than twice as many calories per gram as carbohydrates and proteins do). Fats in the diet are needed for healthy skin and normal growth. Fats also carry certain vitamins to wherever they are needed in the body and provide a reserve supply of energy.

Cooking oils, nuts, fish, and avocados can be healthy sources of fat.

VITAMINS

The discovery of vitamins began early in the 20th century. It is likely that some still are undiscovered. Although vitamins are needed in only small amounts, they are essential for good health. They help keep the body's tissues healthy and its many systems working properly. Each vitamin has specific roles to play. Many reactions in the body require several vitamins, and the lack or excess of any one can interfere with the function of another.

WHAT THEY DO

Vitamin A is needed for good vision, healthy skin, and proper functioning of the immune system.

Vitamin D helps the body use calcium and phosphorus to build strong bones and teeth.

Vitamin E helps protect the body's cells from damage by oxygen.

Vitamin K is necessary for normal blood clotting.

Vitamin C is essential for healthy teeth, gums, and blood vessels. It also helps the body heal wounds and resist infections.

The B vitamins are thiamin, riboflavin, niacin, vitamin B6, vitamin B12, folic acid (folate), pantothenic acid, and biotin. They help turn carbohydrates into energy. They also are needed for a healthy nervous system and muscle coordination.

MINERALS

Minerals are another group of essential nutrients, needed to regulate body processes and fluid balance. Minerals also give structure to bones and teeth. Minerals can be divided into two categories—major and trace—depending on how much the body needs. Major minerals, which are needed in larger amounts, include calcium, phosphorus, magnesium, sulfur, sodium chloride, and potassium. Trace minerals include chromium, copper, fluoride, iodine, iron, manganese, molybdenum, selenium, zinc, and cobalt. Almost all foods contribute to a varied intake of essential minerals.

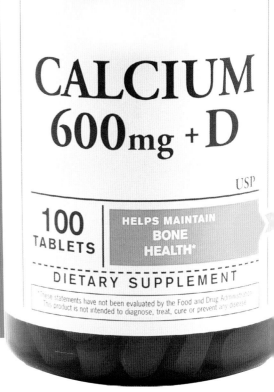

CALCIUM
600mg + D

USP

100 TABLETS

HELPS MAINTAIN
BONE HEALTH*

DIETARY SUPPLEMENT

*These statements have not been evaluated by the Food and Drug Administration. This product is not intended to diagnose, treat, cure or prevent any disease.

WATER

Water takes an active part in many chemical reactions in the body. It is also needed to carry other nutrients, to regulate body temperature, and to help eliminate wastes.

AGRICULTURE

Agriculture is another word for farming. It includes both growing and harvesting crops and raising animals, or livestock. Agriculture provides the food and many raw materials that humans need to survive.

THROUGHOUT THE WORLD

People practice agriculture on farms, on ranches, and in orchards all over the world. Farmers raise crops and livestock in every climate and in all kinds of different soil. Some regions receive a lot of sunlight or rainfall. Others have colder or drier weather. All places have their own kinds of agriculture.

CROP ROTATION

Farmers protect their crops by practicing crop rotation. The same crop should not be planted in the same fields year after year. Doing so can destroy the soil. Certain plants will use up all of the nutrients in the soil. But some plants add necessary nutrients. For example, nitrogen is essential for plant growth. Certain crops, such as clover and soybeans, add nitrogen to the soil. After they are allowed to grow and add the nitrogen to the soil, the next year other crops that need nitrogen can be planted.

ORGANIC FARMS

Many farmers use chemicals and pesticides (chemicals used to kill insects) to help their crops grow. However, these chemicals can harm people and the environment. Organic farming rejects the use of chemicals. Organic farmers use natural methods to protect the soil, help crops thrive, and ward off pests.

An organic farm in Thailand.

A field of soybeans.

A ranch in Argentina.

DIFFERENT REGIONS, DIFFERENT CONDITIONS

If a plant does not have the kind of soil it needs, it may die. Similarly, animals also need to have the right climate and the right food to survive. Farmers try to raise the kinds of livestock and plants that will do well in their region. If they do not have perfect natural conditions, they try to create the best conditions possible. For example, many farmers in dry areas use irrigation, or artificial watering.

THE DEVELOPMENT OF
FARMING

Agriculture has no single, simple origin. It developed independently in many regions of the world. A wide variety of plants and animals were domesticated at different times. Agriculture began in the Middle East more than 10,000 years ago. Perhaps attempts at agriculture were underway even earlier in Southeast Asia. Both of those areas were rich in animals that were suitable for domestication and in varieties of plants, and both have mild climates.

Barley ready for harvest.

THE FIRST CROPS

The first crops in the Middle East probably included grains such as wheat, oats, rye, barley, and millet; and legumes such as peas, lentils, vetch, chickpeas, and horsebeans. Grapes, olives, dates, apples, pears, cherries, and figs were among early domesticated fruits. Early crops in East Asia included millet, rice, Chinese cabbage, and soybeans. In the Americas, corn (maize) and squash were among the earliest domesticated plants.

This ancient Egyptian bas-relief shows a peasant leading his cow.

Chinese cabbage.

FIVE MILESTONES

1 The ancient Mesopotamian cultures—Sumerian, Babylonian, Assyrian, and Chaldean—developed an increasingly complex and rich agricultural system that freed many people from farming. As a result, the first cities arose in Mesopotamia.

2 Ancient farming is clearly recorded in Egypt, where it flourished along the Nile River. Egyptian farmers developed drainage and irrigation techniques through construction of a system of dikes and canals.

3 The Romans discovered and carefully noted relatively sophisticated techniques such as grafting and budding, crop rotation, and the use of fertilizers.

4 By the end of the Middle Ages most of the tillable land of Europe was cleared, drained, and in cultivation. At that time the transition from medieval to modern agricultural practices began. This transition is called the agricultural revolution. New foods entered European farming. During the 16th century the potato and maize (corn), imported from the New World, and rice, introduced earlier from Asia, came under cultivation in Europe.

5 About 200 years ago the Industrial Revolution brought great changes to agriculture. In the past people had used hand tools and animals to help them plant and harvest. Machines invented during the Industrial Revolution made that work easier.

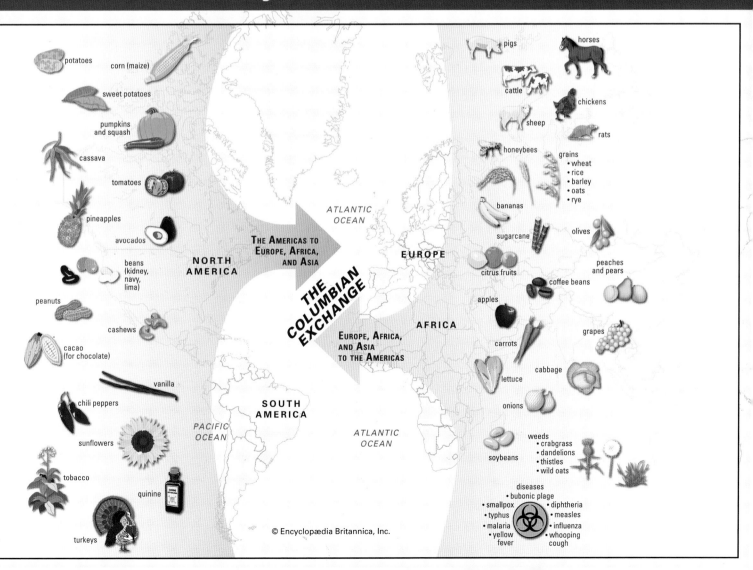

© Encyclopædia Britannica, Inc.

DOMESTICATION

The human race's progress on Earth has been due in part to the animals that people have been able to utilize throughout history. Such domesticated animals carry people and their burdens. They pull machinery and help cultivate fields. They provide food and clothing.

THE DOG

There seems to be little doubt that the dog was the first animal domesticated by humans. Its bones are common in campsites of the late Neolithic that date back more than 10,000 years. At least five different kinds of dogs similar to the household pets of today have been identified from these remains. The beginnings of their domestication must therefore date many thousands of years earlier than that.

Herd of zebu cattle.

HERD ANIMALS

Cattle, sheep, pigs, goats, and horses—the most important and widespread of the domestic animals—are all hoofed grass eaters and can be kept in herds. All of them were first mastered by the early peoples of southwestern Asia. It has been suggested that the grassy plains of that region began slowly eroding some 10,000 years ago. Humans were forced to share smaller and smaller oases of fertile land with wild animals. People gradually learned how to control the animals. Some animals were bred in captivity, and from them the domestic strains developed.

AROUND THE WORLD

Of the millions of species in the world, relatively few have been domesticated. Here are some familiar domesticated animals and the places where remains of their earliest ancestors were found.

- Southwest Asia: cattle, sheep, pigs, goats, camels, horses, and donkeys

- Southeast Asia: water buffalo, oxen, and chickens

- Northern Europe: reindeer

- Africa: cats, donkeys, and guinea fowl

- South America: llamas, alpacas, and guinea pigs

- North and Central America: turkeys

Guinea fowl.

MODERN FARMS

Agriculture developed more rapidly in the 20th century than in all previous history. By 2000, global agricultural production was 1.6 times greater than the total production level obtained in 1950, after more than 10,000 years of agricultural history. Much of this surge can be attributed to improved breeding techniques, the expansion of arable land, and mechanization on the farm. The practice of sustainable agriculture, such as the regulation of fertilizers, the implementation of proper irrigation methods, and the use of crop rotation, has also helped.

Commercial farm.

SUBSISTENCE FARMING

Today, about 1.3 billion, or about one in five, people are farmers. Most of them struggle along as subsistence farmers. This means that they raise plants and animals to provide for their families, usually having little or nothing left over to sell or trade for other goods. Subsistence farming is common in crowded, poorer, less-developed countries and in depressed areas even in advanced countries. In this type of farming, a farm may be less than 1 acre (0.4 hectare) in size and the land of poor quality. The family that works such a farm usually coaxes it to provide enough to live on only through intensive hand labor.

Subsistence farmer.

COMMERCIAL FARMS

In more-developed, less-crowded countries, such as the United States, Australia, and Canada, a single farm may reach as far as the eye can see in any direction and may be run by a large corporation that uses only the latest machines and technology. Such commercial farms are the big agricultural producers in more-developed countries. They are operated much like other industries. Many are family run, but the family functions as management for the parent corporation.

SEE A FAMILY FARM IN THE VR VIEWER.

Rice terraces in Vietnam.

Diversified, general farming, in which many crops and different kinds of animals are raised, is the traditional farming practiced in Western countries with temperate climates. These farms are often composed of land claimed from forest and prairie.

A specialized farm is a commercial farm that produces a major crop or a few major crops that account for half or more of the farm's gross sales. These are crops best suited to the land and climate and to the skill and financial ability of the farmer.

Farms on flat to rolling lands are usually used for row crops or grains. Rocky, irregular lands are usually used as pasture, left wooded, or used for tree farms.

Dryland farming, practiced on prairies and other places where rainfall is light (less than 20 inches, or 50 centimeters), is common in many parts of North America and Europe. Soils are generally deep and rich, but yields vary because rainfall is not only light but also uneven from year to year. Crops planted in such areas include winter wheat and grain sorghum.

Sorghum.

Pineapple.

Tropical farming, practiced where the climate is predominantly warm and wet, is common throughout Latin America, Africa, India, Australia, and Southeast Asia. The amount of land suitable for tropical farming is limited and requires careful management to be productive and sustaining. The soil is leached of nutrients rapidly by the heavy rainfalls typical of the tropics. Tropical crops include coconut, palm oil, rice, sugarcane, pineapple, sisal, cocoa, tea, coffee, jute, rubber, pepper, banana, and breadfruit.

FARMING METHODS AROUND THE WORLD

SHIFTING AGRICULTURE

While technology is advancing in many parts of the world, some cultures in sparsely populated tropical areas still practice a shifting system of agriculture. This system is a type of slash-and-burn agriculture, in which land is cleared of plant life, which is burned to add some nutrients to the soil. This is followed by planting. When the land is exhausted, it is abandoned and new clearings are slashed and burned.

PLANTATION AGRICULTURE

A plantation is a large area of land that is usually privately or government owned and employs resident labor to cultivate a single commercial crop. Plantation agriculture is generally found in tropical and subtropical regions.

Banana plantation.

FLOODPLAIN FARMING

Farming in the tropics often includes floodplain cropping with periodic irrigation. A river's floodplain is the area on either side of the river over which it deposits soil when it floods. Farming is practiced along the floodplains of rivers such as the Nile in Egypt and large waterways in Asia, where paddies are formed by terracing.

A rice field in Thailand.

BURNING-GRAZING

In many parts of the world grasses cover the land as far as the eye can see. Livestock grazing is ideal in these areas, which include the prairies of the western United States the lowland plains (the Pampas) of South America, the tropical savannas of Africa, and the steppes of Asia.

The Pampas.

DESERT FARMING

Tempted by the Sun and long growing season, many countries have converted their deserts into green oases for growing crops. Large irrigation projects transport water for many miles to produce large crops in places such as the interior desert valleys of California, Arizona, Colorado, and Texas in the United States.

DIVERSIFIED GENERAL FARMING

The farming traditional to Western cultures in temperate regions is diversified general farming. In this type of farming a variety of crops is grown, including corn, small grains, orchard fruits, and soybeans.

PRAIRIE FARMING

Much prairie land is used for the burning-grazing agriculture described earlier. Large acreages are usually devoted to a single crop or only a few. The prairie wheat fields of Canada and the cornfields of the United States are examples.

A prairie in Alberta.

Cattle at an agricultural fair.

AGRICULTURAL FAIRS

Each year there are an estimated 19,000 agricultural and livestock fairs around the world. About one fourth of these are held in the United States, and many of them are small, local exhibitions such as county or district fairs.

EARLY AGRICULTURAL FAIRS

Agricultural fairs evolved in Europe and North America from the annual sheep shearings held by estate owners in the late 18th and early 19th centuries. Among the earliest agricultural fairs in Europe was the National Show of 1821 in London. The first significant United States livestock exposition was the Berkshire Cattle Show of 1810 in New England.

This poster was shown at an agricultural fair in Louisiana in 1938.

EARLY STATE FAIRS

In 1841 the first state fair was held at Syracuse, N.Y., and within the next two decades hundreds of state and local fairs sprang up. Some of the oldest state fairs are those held in Michigan since 1849; Pennsylvania, Ohio, and Wisconsin (1851); Indiana (1852); Illinois (1853); and Iowa (1854).

AGRICULTURAL FAIRS TODAY

Since 1900 the agricultural fair has grown steadily in popularity, and there has been a trend toward expanded industrial and commercial exhibits, carnival midways with sideshows and rides, and large grandstand entertainment programs. Among the largest state and county fairs, with annual attendance exceeding one million each, are Texas, Minnesota, Wisconsin, Los Angeles County, Illinois, Michigan, Ohio, and California. In Canada the Pacific National Exhibition at Vancouver, B.C., and the Canadian National Exhibition at Toronto both attract well over a million visitors every year.

A parade at the National Western Livestock Show in Denver, Colorado.

ANNUAL LIVESTOCK SHOWS

There are a number of large, annual livestock shows in the United States: the American Royal Livestock Exposition in Kansas City, Missouri; the National Western Livestock Show in Denver, Colorado; and the Ak-Sar-Ben Livestock Show in Omaha, Nebraska.

FARM MACHINERY

Farm machines have increased human productivity enormously. One farmer on a cotton picker, for example, can harvest as much in a day as 100 people working by hand. Before agriculture was mechanized in the United States, ten farmworkers were needed to feed one person in a city. Today one farmer's output can feed more than 100 city dwellers. Conditions are similar in other economically developed nations. An important aspect of farm machinery that is not often recognized is that it has made modern social and economic organization possible by freeing large numbers of people from food and fiber production for other work, such as manufacturing.

A VARIETY OF USES

As agriculture developed, farmers applied machines to all operations. They mechanized soil tilling, fertilizing, and irrigating; planting and cultivating; animal feeding; pest, weed, and disease control; harvesting; and crop processing.

TILLING THE SOIL

Tillage is defined as any manipulation of the soil. Soil is usually tilled before planting. For most crops farmers apply fertilizers to the soil if needed. The fertilizers improve crop growth and yields. In dry areas field crops are watered by irrigation.

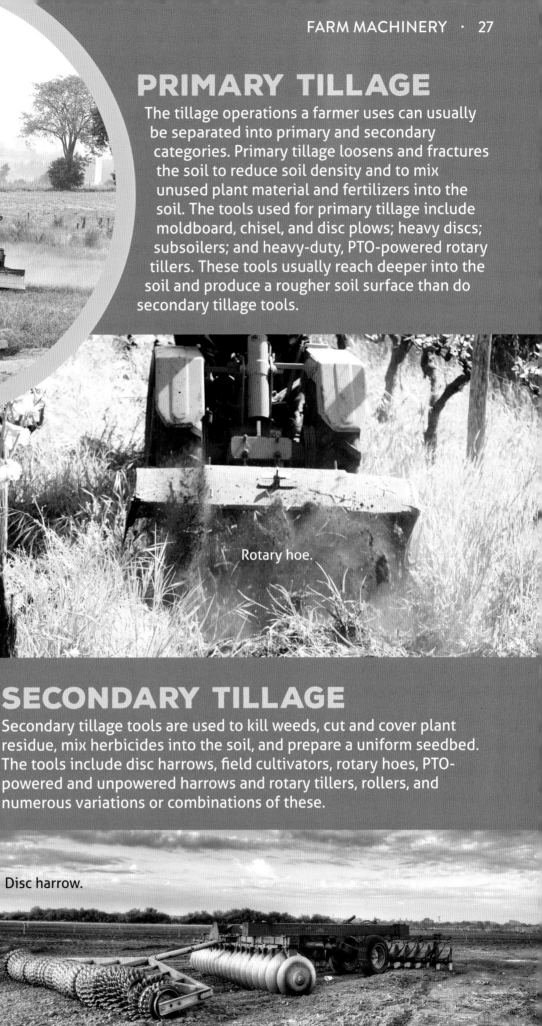

Rotary tiller.

PRIMARY TILLAGE

The tillage operations a farmer uses can usually be separated into primary and secondary categories. Primary tillage loosens and fractures the soil to reduce soil density and to mix unused plant material and fertilizers into the soil. The tools used for primary tillage include moldboard, chisel, and disc plows; heavy discs; subsoilers; and heavy-duty, PTO-powered rotary tillers. These tools usually reach deeper into the soil and produce a rougher soil surface than do secondary tillage tools.

Rotary hoe.

SECONDARY TILLAGE

Secondary tillage tools are used to kill weeds, cut and cover plant residue, mix herbicides into the soil, and prepare a uniform seedbed. The tools include disc harrows, field cultivators, rotary hoes, PTO-powered and unpowered harrows and rotary tillers, rollers, and numerous variations or combinations of these.

Disc harrow.

FERTILIZING

Crops may be nourished with manure—refuse from barns and barnyards, including animal wastes and straw—or with chemical fertilizers in solid, liquid, or gaseous form. A manure spreader is a four-wheeled, or two-wheeled, wagon drawn behind a tractor. A drag-chain conveyor at the bottom of the wagon box pushes the manure to the rear, where it is successively shredded by a pair of beaters before being spread by rotating spiral fins.

Manure spreader.

PLANTING

The grain drill, or seed drill, one of the oldest farm machines, plants seed at a controlled depth and in accurate amounts to obtain optimum crop yields. The earliest known grain drill, which was invented in Mesopotamia before tillage, consisted of a wood plow equipped with a seed hopper and a tube that conveyed the seed to the furrow. Modern grain drills generally have several furrow openers evenly spaced to open the soil for the seed and sometimes short lengths of chain that drag behind to cover the seed.

Seed drill.

CULTIVATING

Cultivators are usually mounted on the back of a tractor and stir the soil between crop rows, promoting crop growth and destroying weeds. Rotary hoes are used for early cultivation of row crops like corn, cotton, soybeans, and potatoes. Rotary hoes are a fast, economical means of controlling small weeds and breaking a surface crust to improve crop emergence.

Cultivator.

HARVESTING

A combine, a modern harvesting machine.

Harvesting machinery has progressively mechanized the farmer's tasks. The first popular mechanical reaper was invented in 1831 in the United States by Cyrus Hall McCormick. The reaper replaced the scythe, a long-handled, bladed hand tool that farmers had used for centuries to cut grain and grassy plants. In spite of the extensive hand labor involved in their use, reapers cut in half the time needed for harvesting.

Cyrus McCormick.

IRRIGATION

Irrigation is what farmers do when they add water to their fields. Irrigation takes the place of rainfall in dry regions. It can greatly increase farm production. However, irrigation can also cause problems with the environment.

GETTING WATER

Most water for irrigation comes from the ground or from a river. Farmers get water from the ground by digging a well. Then they lift or pump the water from the well. Farmers may get water from a river by digging a channel, or path, from the riverbank. They also may collect river water by building a dam across the river. Water collects behind the dam in an artificial lake called a reservoir. After getting water, farmers move water to the farm fields through canals or pipelines.

APPLYING WATER

The next step in irrigation is to deliver the water to the plants in the fields. There are many ways to do this. They include surface, subsurface, and overhead irrigation.

Drip irrigation is being used for this lettuce crop.

SURFACE IRRIGATION

Surface irrigation systems apply water directly onto the soil surface. One kind of surface irrigation is called flood irrigation. This method floods the growing plants with water. Rice is the main crop irrigated by flood irrigation. A second kind of surface irrigation is called furrow irrigation. Water flows into the furrows and then soaks into the earth. Potatoes, sugar beets, cotton, and corn are often irrigated by furrow irrigation. A third kind of surface irrigation is called drip, or trickle, irrigation. Pipes with holes in them drip water onto plants. This method is good for dry regions.

These onions are irrigated from water flowing through siphon tubes.

SUBSURFACE IRRIGATION

Subsurface irrigation systems apply water beneath the soil's surface. Buried pipes with holes in them deliver water to the plants. This method is good for fruit plants and garden vegetables.

Overheard irrigation system.

OVERHEAD IRRIGATION

Overhead irrigation systems spray or sprinkle water over crops. Rotary sprinklers are a common form of overhead irrigation. They sprinkle water in a wide circle while moving slowly across a field.

Flooding has eroded topsoil at this farm.

SOIL CONSERVATION

Whenever land is stripped of its plant cover, soil is inevitably lost by erosion, the so-called silent thief. A single rainstorm can wash away centuries-old accumulations of soil from neglected or badly managed fields. Topsoil is an extremely valuable natural resource. Under this thin blanket of rich dirt and humus, in which plants grow best, is a less fertile material called subsoil. If the surface layer of topsoil is blown or washed away, the remaining subsoil cannot support plant life, and the farm must eventually be abandoned. To help prevent the start of erosion and ensure that agriculture is sustainable, farmers have used a variety of conservation measures.

Terraced rice fields.

CONTOURING AND TERRACING

Contouring involves plowing, planting, and cultivating sloping fields around hillsides, with curving furrows horizontal to the hill, instead of furrows running straight uphill and downhill. The curved furrows catch rainfall and allow much of it to soak into the ground. They also catch soil washing down from higher levels. On long slopes a low ridge, or terrace, thrown along the outer side of the slope catches soil and rainwater and retards runoff. Encouraging plant growth on a terrace helps hold soil.

STRIP-CROPPING

Strip-cropping is a practice in which strips of close-growing plants, such as grasses or clover, are alternated between strips of clean-tilled row crops, such as corn and soybeans. The strips of close-growing plants hold water and keep it from eroding the cultivated strip below. These strips are planted on the contour.

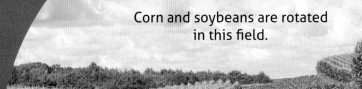

Corn and soybeans are rotated in this field.

CROP ROTATION

Planting different crops each year on a piece of land keeps the soil productive. One crop can benefit the next. For example, soybeans add nitrogen to soil whereas corn removes it. Rotating corn and soybean crops is a common practice in modern farming.

COVER CROPS

Land is kept covered in winter and summer with either a growing crop or the residue, such as corn stalks, from the crop previously grown. When cover crops are plowed under for green manuring, the plant foods added to the soil improve its water-holding capacity and increase its fertility.

Harvested corn field.

PEST CONTROL

Organisms considered harmful to humans or their interests are called pests. They include plants or animals that carry disease, cause disease, or destroy crops or structures. The term pest may refer to insects, viruses, and bacteria that carry or cause disease. It may also refer to organisms that destroy crops or man-made structures. Plants, such as weeds or fungi, and vertebrates, such as rats, mice, and birds, are sometimes called pests when they destroy crops or stored foods. The elimination of pests or the inhibition of their reproduction, development, or migration is known as pest control.

Small planes and helicopters can be used to spray pesticides.

This tractor is spraying pesticides.

CHEMICAL CONTROL

The most common method of pest control is the use of pesticides—chemicals that either kill pests or inhibit their development. In the 1960s and 1970s, public objections were raised over the indiscriminate use of pesticides. The Environmental Protection Agency (EPA) was created in 1970 to ascertain past damage and possible future damage that could occur to the environment as the result of widespread pesticide use, and to set up programs to combat environmental problems.

BIOLOGICAL CONTROL

The biological control of pests involves exposing them to predators or parasites. Biological pest control was used by the ancient Chinese, who used predacious ants to control plant-eating insects. The modern era of biological pest control began in 1888, when the vedalia beetle was imported from Australia to California to control the cottony-cushion scale insect. This biological control project saved the citrus-fruit industry.

Vedalia beetle.

These strawberry beds are protected by mesh, a physical control method.

OTHER METHODS OF CONTROL

Crops are sometimes protected from harmful pests through diverse planting techniques. Crop rotation, for example, prevents the development of fungus and bacterium populations. Open-area planting relies on the wind to hinder flies and other insects that damage vegetable crops. Physical or mechanical control methods are effective against some pests. Such controls include sticky barriers, heat killing (for storage pests), and flooding (for ground pests).

CORN

After wheat and rice, farmers the world over use more land for corn than for any other grain crop. More than 319 million acres (129 million hectares) of corn are planted worldwide each year. Most of the corn grown is the coarser kind called field corn. It is not grown for people to eat. Farmers feed it to pigs, cattle, and other livestock.

A THREE-YEAR CYCLE

Corn draws heavily on nutrients in the soil. Production is higher when corn crops are rotated on a three-year cycle. The first year a legume, such as alfalfa or sweet clover, builds up the soil with nitrogen and humus. Corn, planted the next year, thrives on these nutrients. The third year farmers plant a small grain, such as oats or rye. Small-grain crops help protect the soil; they reduce soil erosion and take up nitrates that would otherwise leach out of the soil and then contaminate water supplies.

WHEAT

Wheat is one of the oldest cereal crops. It was cultivated as long as 9,000 years ago in the Euphrates Valley of the Middle East. Egyptian pharoahs were buried with an ancient variety of wheat to help nourish them on their voyage into the afterlife. As a food crop essential to the making of bread, pastry, and pasta, wheat products are eaten by many people at every meal.

FIVE FAST FACTS

① Five bushels of wheat, when processed, will produce more than a barrel of flour.

② Wheat keeps so well that it can be shipped around the world or stored for years.

③ Weather that is comfortable for humans is also good for wheat. Wheat needs 12 to 15 inches (31 to 38 centimeters) of water to produce a good crop. It grows best when temperatures are warm, from 70° to 75° F (21° to 24°C), but not too hot.

④ Most of the world's wheat is grown in the temperate areas of the Northern Hemisphere.

⑤ Because wheat is a hardy crop, it can sometimes be grown where other crops fail.

RICE

Fully half the population of the world depends on rice for fundamental, daily nutrition. In East Asia, Central Asia, the islands of the western Pacific, and much of Latin America, rice is the basic component of most meals. The name rice is applied both to the edible, starchy cereal grain and to the plant from which it is produced. The number of varieties of the cultivated rice plant is staggering. In India alone there exist more than 8,000 varieties, and in the Philippines there are more than 3,500.

THE HISTORY OF RICE

Historians have traced the origin of rice cultivation to India in about 3000 BC. From there it spread in all directions—to Japan, the Philippines, Persia, and Egypt—rivaling other grains, such as millet, barley, and wheat, in popularity.

POTATOES

Considered by most botanists to be a native of the Peruvian-Bolivian Andes, the potato is one of the main food crops of the world. The edible part of a potato plant is the tuber, the swollen ends of its underground stems.

PACKED WITH NUTRITION

Easily digested, potatoes also have a high nutritional value. A potato tuber is about 78 percent water and about 18 percent starch (carbohydrates). The rest is protein, minerals, and about 0.1 percent fat. Potatoes contain many vitamins, including vitamin C, riboflavin, thiamine, and niacin. Among the many minerals found in potatoes are calcium, potassium, phosphorus, and magnesium. Because they are notably lacking in sodium, potatoes are sometimes suggested for inclusion in low-sodium diets.

ORCHARDS

Orcharding is an intensive method of fruit and nut tree cropping. It demands skill and effort to be done successfully. The first orchards came into being in the temperate regions of Europe, Asia, and North America. Crops such as apples, pears, plums, apricots, and cherries are grown in orchards.

Pear orchard.

Apple orchard.

WHERE ORCHARDS ARE FOUND

In the United States many orchards are found concentrated in California, Florida, and Washington. There are extensive pear orchards in the Rhône River valley of Europe and apple and pear orchards in northern Italy. Southern Australia, South Africa, and southern Argentina are also areas of fruit orcharding. China, the world's largest apple producer, grows more than 40 million tons of that fruit per year.

Almond orchard

PRINCIPAL CROPS

In the United States and Europe almond, apple, citrus, pear, peach, plum, apricot, cherry, pecan, and walnut are the principal orchard-grown crops. Although grapes are sometimes grown in orchards, along with some other fruit, they are more usually grown in vineyards.

FIVE FAST FACTS

1 The science and practice of growing fruit is called pomology.

2 Fruits are relatively expensive because of their production and marketing costs.

3 The steps of growing fruit include planting, care, harvesting, packing, storing, and shipping.

4 The aim of commercial fruit tree production is to achieve the highest yield with the least labor. Dwarf and semidwarf trees are planted close together in hedgerows, which are "walls" of trees that are supported by posts and wires.

5 Care in commercial plantings is intensive and highly mechanized, from spraying and pruning to harvesting and grading. The close spacing makes it necessary to spray efficiently and to utilize mechanical devices that provide maximum yields.

Angus cows.

CATTLE

In many areas of the world, cattle have long been among the most important domestic animals. They are raised as livestock on farms. Their meat is called beef. Their milk is drunk and is used to make dairy products such as butter, cheese, and yogurt. Their hides are used to make leather. Their dung is used in fertilizer and has been burned for fuel, while their fat has been used as tallow to make candles and soap.

FOUR FAST FACTS

1 Cattle are of such economic importance that the word—derived from the Latin *capitale*—was once a synonym for "property" or "wealth."

2 India was the world's leading cattle-producing nation at the beginning of the 21st century, followed by Brazil.

3 Cattle are ruminants—animals with multichambered stomachs that enable them to digest plant matter that is too coarse for most mammals to eat.

4 Domestic cattle average about 3 feet (1 meter) tall at the shoulders. Depending on the breed, mature bulls weigh 1,000–4,000 pounds (450–1,800 kilograms) and cows 800–2,400 pounds (350–1,100 kilograms).

BEEF CATTLE

Beef cattle are produced in many countries of the world. They are found in almost every section of the United States. In the Western regions cattle graze over a vast area. Beef cattle breeds are more muscular in appearance than dairy cattle. They have been bred to convert the feed they eat into a quality meat product. Some breeds of beef cattle are the Angus, Brahmans, Charolais, and Herefords.

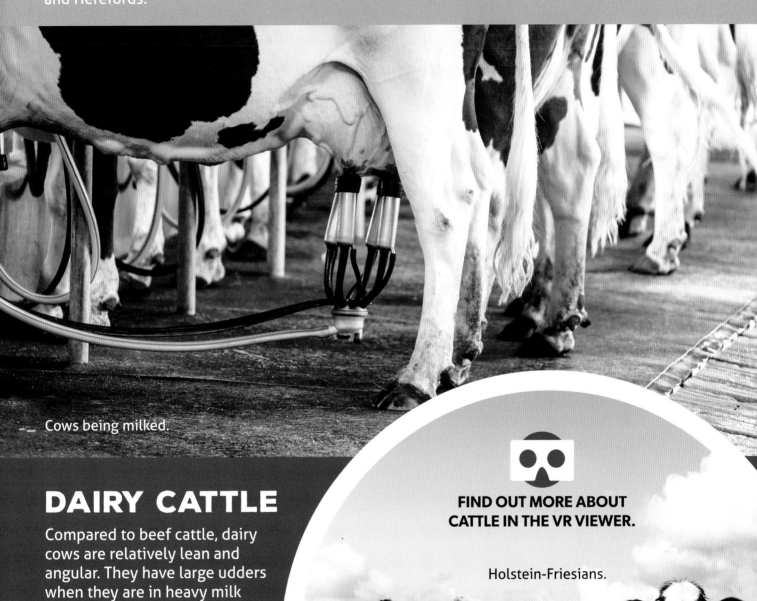

Cows being milked.

DAIRY CATTLE

Compared to beef cattle, dairy cows are relatively lean and angular. They have large udders when they are in heavy milk production. Ideally, a dairy cow produces milk for 10 months followed by a dry period of about two months, when her body rests and stores energy for the next lactation, or milking, period. Breeds of dairy cattle include Ayrshires, Guernseys, Holstein-Friesians, and Jerseys.

FIND OUT MORE ABOUT CATTLE IN THE VR VIEWER.

Holstein-Friesians.

MILK

The basic food of all newborn mammals is produced by their mothers as a liquid called milk. This milk contains all the food, including protein, fat, sugar, and other nutrients, a young mammal requires for a long period of time. The human being is the only mammal that continues to use milk and milk products after infancy. Before recorded history humans learned to keep animals and take from them extra milk not needed by their offspring. In various parts of the world, goats, reindeer, donkeys, yaks, water buffalo, and sheep are domesticated and milked. In most countries, however, milk is provided by dairy cows.

WHAT'S IN MILK?

Fresh whole milk is about 88 percent water. The remainder is made up of solids that contain fat, protein, and lactose (milk sugar). These give milk its color, taste, and nutritional value. Fat makes up approximately 3 percent of whole milk and supplies the body with calories for energy. Most of the 150 calories in an 8-ounce (237-milliliter) glass of milk come from this fat. The protein in milk is in the form of casein and whey protein. Protein is needed for tissue building, and about 40 percent of the daily protein required for a young person is supplied by a quart (0.95 liter) of milk. Lactose is a carbohydrate that is easily burned for energy.

MILK'S MANY FORMS

Milk and milk products are drunk and eaten in many forms, including buttermilk, cheese, yogurt, and butter. Milk can be reduced to powder, concentrated in a thick liquid, and used in cooking. Fresh milk sours quickly, but, when changed into forms such as cheese, it can be kept for a long time.

This woman milks a yak.

SHEEP

Among the most valuable of all the domestic animals are the sheep. They provide humans with meat. They also give wool for cloth. Young sheep, or lambs, provide lamb pelts which are used for fur. In some countries, people drink sheep's milk. Many people use sheep's milk to make cheese.

FIVE FAST FACTS

① The chief sheep-raising countries of the world are China, Australia, New Zealand, and the United Kingdom.

② Sheep are naturally hill animals. They like it best where it is high and dry.

③ Sheep eat grasses and other plants. They like to graze over wide areas of pasture.

④ Domestic ewes (female sheep) bear one or two lambs in the spring.

⑤ Wild sheep are relatives of goats, and it is not always easy to tell the two apart. Sheep never have beards. Goats often do.

Angora goats.

GOATS

Goats are hoofed mammals with hollow horns. Like sheep, they are ruminants and eat grasses and shrubs. Some goats are wild, while others are raised by humans for their milk, cheese, wool, meat, and leather. Goat's milk differs from cow's milk in the smaller size of its fat globules and in its softer curd. It is also easier to digest than cow's milk. Goat cheeses are made in many countries. Goats can live on coarse, thin plant growth and are often raised on land that is not fertile enough to support cattle or sheep.

DOMESTIC GOATS

The six major breeds of domestic goat are descended from the wild, or bezoar, goat. This species was probably native to Iran or Central Asia (where it is still found today). Domestic goats are now raised in most regions of the world. The most common domestic breeds are the Angora, Cashmere, French-Alpine, Nubian, Saanen, and Toggenburg. Different breeds are raised for their milk, wool, or meat.

POULTRY

Domesticated birds that are raised for their meat, eggs, and feathers are collectively called poultry. Chickens are by far the largest single source of poultry meat and eggs in most countries. Other common poultry birds are turkeys, ducks, geese, guinea fowl, and pigeons and their nestlings (called squabs). Pheasants and other game birds are also raised.

Chickens at a traditional farm.

EARLY POULTRY FARMING

The methods of early poultry farmers were quite different from those of the modern industry. Flocks of chickens were raised on farms and fed on the grains and by-products of crop farming. Farmers either hatched their chicks on the farm or purchased them from a local hatchery and raised them during the spring months. During warm weather the chicks were allowed to roam over the farm. Young male chickens were used for meat, whereas the young females were kept as layers.

MODERN POULTRY FARMING

In the beginning of the 19th century, the demand for chicken meat and eggs grew, enough so that a mass-produced industry developed. Currently in most industrialized nations, the earlier methods of poultry raising have been replaced by commercialization, specialization, and concentration of poultry production, especially the production of chickens and turkeys. There are now egg-producing firms that specialize in the mass production of eggs; breeding farms that specialize in producing hatching eggs; poultry growers that specialize in raising broilers, turkeys, or other specific poultry types; and various firms that specialize in egg hatching, feed manufacturing, and transportation.

Chicks at a modern chicken farm.

EGGS

Commercially raised hens can lay around 300 eggs a year. If a hen mates with a rooster before laying eggs, the eggs will be fertilized and will develop into chicks. But hens can lay eggs without mating. These unfertilized eggs are the eggs that people eat.

Turkeys.

Landrace pig.

PIGS

Wild pigs existed as far back as 36 million years ago. The hunting of wild pigs by early humans was often depicted in Western European cave and rock paintings dating back thousands of years. Domestic pigs probably descended from one species—the Eurasian wild boar (*Sus scrofa*). Domestication of the pig coincided with the formation of the first permanent human settlements. As a domestic animal the pig is a source of a wide variety of meats, high-quality leather, durable bristles for many kinds of brushes, and hundreds of medical products.

WHAT THEY EAT

Pigs are omnivores. The wild species eat a wide variety of foods, including leaves, roots, fruit, reptiles, rodents, and carrion. Domestic pigs are normally fed diets of corn, grain, root and tuber crops, dairy by-products, commercial feeds, and edible garbage.

FROM ANCIENT TO MODERN

Since ancient times there have been two basic methods for keeping domestic pigs. The first method was the pen rearing of pigs in enclosures or sties. In the second method the animals were allowed to roam at will, rooting and scavenging for whatever food they could find—a method that is still practiced in many developing countries. Modern husbandry methods generally include pasture feeding, confinement feeding, or a combination of the two. In the United States there has been a pronounced trend from pasture rearing to confinement-feeding methods.

Berkshire piglets.

FIND OUT MORE ABOUT PIGS IN THE VR VIEWER.

Duroc pigs.

PIG BREEDS

By means of selection and controlled mating, more than 300 pig breeds have been raised. The Landrace is known for producing large litters of piglets and crosses well with other breeds. The Berkshire is renowned for the quality of its meat. The Duroc is an especially popular breed in the United States and Australia. Like the Landrace, the Duroc is often used for cross-breeding; in fact, Landrace/Duroc crosses are highly valued in the bacon trade.

THE
MEAT INDUSTRY

The meat industry in the industrialized world is the largest segment of the food industry. Its main purpose is to obtain livestock from producers and to process the livestock into meat and nonfood products. Meat-processing plants perform a variety of operations, ranging from slaughter to processing and sale.

This 1908 photograph shows workers at a meat-packing plant in Indiana.

THE ORIGINS OF MEAT PACKING

The term meat packing originated in colonial times from the practice of salting and packing pork in wooden barrels for storage or shipment to Europe. Colonial meat shops were the first retail meat markets. As cities grew, small packing plants were established. Animals were often driven on hoof from the production areas to railroad heads, then moved by rail to large terminal livestock markets.

TRANSPORTATION AND REFRIGERATION

Transportation and refrigeration contributed to the development of the meat industry. Packing plants were built in large cities so that the highly perishable meat products could be moved quickly to the consumer. Before the advent of mechanical refrigeration, slaughter and processing were limited to the winter season, except in areas where ice was available for storage in the summer months. The first mechanical refrigeration system was installed in a meat-packing plant in 1880, and the first refrigerated rail car was placed in service in the 1870s. By the early 1900s large meat-packing plants were established in all the major cities of the United States.

MODERN MEAT-PACKING PLANTS

Modern meat-packing plants are located closer to the areas of livestock production because it is more economical and feasible to ship meat rather than to transport live animals. Often located in open country, most of these plants are highly specialized. With the relocation of packing plants near the source of livestock production, most livestock are now sold by the producer directly to the packing plant rather than to brokers.

AQUACULTURE

The growing of plants and animals on land for food and other products is agriculture. Raising animals and plants in the water is aquaculture. Practiced since ancient times in many parts of the world, aquaculture embraces such diverse activities as the Chinese tradition of growing carp in ponds, the harvesting and processing of seaweed in Iceland, and the artificial culture of pearls—a Japanese invention.

THE BENEFITS OF AQUACULTURE

Aquaculture is regarded as one possible solution to the world's food supply problems. The quantity of tillable land is limited and shrinking everywhere. But more than two thirds of the globe is covered with water; the supply of food animals and plants that may be grown there is almost limitless. In contrast to agriculture, which is practiced on the land's surface only, aquaculture is three-dimensional. Within the same vertical region several different crops can be grown at once—near the water surface, on the bottom, and in the area between.

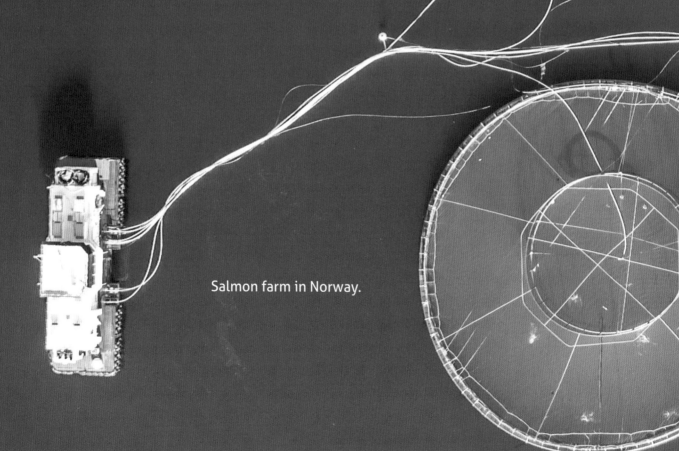

Salmon farm in Norway.

ANIMAL AQUACULTURE

Aquaculturists keep their animals captive by such means as ponds, tanks, and underwater enclosures. In some areas fish are artificially bred, released into the wild, and then recaptured as adults. This is done in enclosed areas such as the Caspian Sea, where sturgeon are raised for their flesh and their eggs. Foods for the captive animals are chosen to yield maximum growth. In recent years the diets of many cultured fish have been supplemented with vitamins.

PLANT AQUACULTURE

Some water plants are as systematically cultivated as agricultural crops. Since the 17th century, for example, the Japanese have grown amanori (edible red algae) near estuaries, places where rivers meet the sea. The Chinese have also controlled and organized the culture of water plants such as kelp. Similar practices are developing in the Philippines, and interest is growing in many other parts of the world.

Algae farm in Indonesia.

Kelp farm in Tanzania.

SUGAR

A liking for sweet things seems natural to people everywhere. In ancient times people satisfied their desire for sweets with honey. Today sugar is the most widely used sweetener.

Sugarcane field.

Sugar beet.

HEALTH ISSUES

Today sugar is associated with a number of health problems. It is known, for example, that excessive consumption of sugar can contribute to obesity and promote tooth decay. In addition, sugar has been associated with hyperactivity in children and hypertension in adults. Nevertheless it remains a popular food and flavoring.

WHERE DOES SUGAR COME FROM?

Almost all commercially made sugar comes from sugarcane or sugar beets. Sugarcane is a giant, thick, perennial grass cultivated in tropical and subtropical regions worldwide for its sweet sap. The sugar beet (*Beta vulgaris*) is a species of beet that can be grown in temperate or cold climates, where sugarcane will not grow. Sugar is stored in the tapering, white roots of the beet. The sugar from sugarcane and sugar beets is transformed into commercial sugar in two stages. First, the sugar is extracted from the plants; then, it is refined.

CHOCOLATE

As a food and a flavoring, chocolate is widely popular. People almost everywhere enjoy chocolate candies, pastries, and drinks. Chocolate is made from the seeds, or "beans," of the tropical cacao tree. The beans grow inside leathery pods that are found both on the trunk and on the branches of the tree. Workers cut the pods from the tree trunks with large heavy knives called machetes and from the branches with long-handled knives. The purple or creamy-white beans are shelled from the pod, which is about the size of a small cucumber.

FOUR FAST FACTS

1 When shelled from the pod, the chocolate bean has a raw bitter taste.

2 Chocolate was for many centuries enjoyed chiefly as a beverage.

3 Chocolate's popularity began in the Americas where the cacao tree grew wild. The tree was cultivated by the Maya, Toltec, and Aztec more than 3,000 years ago.

4 The processes for making smooth, tasty chocolate intended for eating were invented in the 1800s.

FOOD PRESERVATION

Food preservation refers to any of a number of methods by which food is kept from spoilage after harvest or slaughter. Such practices date to prehistoric times. Among the oldest methods of preservation are drying, refrigeration, and fermentation. Modern methods include canning, pasteurization, freezing, irradiation, and the addition of chemicals. Advances in packaging materials have played an important role in modern food preservation.

LOW-TEMPERATURE PRESERVATION

Storage at low temperatures prolongs the shelf life of many foods. In general, low temperatures reduce the growth rates of microorganisms and slow many of the physical and chemical reactions that occur in foods. Freezing and frozen storage provide an excellent means of preserving the nutritional quality of foods.

CANNING

Selected crop varieties are grown specially for canning purposes. A typical canning operation involves cleaning, filling, exhausting, can sealing, heat processing, cooking, labeling, casing, and storage. Most of these operations are performed using high-speed, automatic machines.

Canning factory.

These machines are used to pasteurize milk.

PASTEURIZATION

Pasteurization is the application of heat to a food product in order to destroy disease-producing microorganisms, to inactivate spoilage-causing enzymes, and to reduce or destroy spoilage microorganisms.

DEHYDRATION

Dehydration, or drying, of foods has long been practiced commercially in the production of spaghetti and other starch products. As a result of advances made during World War II, the technique has been applied to a growing list of food products, including fruits, vegetables, skim milk, potatoes, soup mixes, and meats.

FERMENTATION

Fermentation is a chemical change in animal and vegetable matter brought about by certain microorganisms. The products of fermentation have been used since earliest times. Early humans discovered that aged meat has a more pleasing flavor than freshly killed meat. Leavened bread is as old as agriculture. Cheese, which involves the fermentation of milk or cream, is another ancient food.

Fermented vegetables.

TEST WHAT YOU KNOW

1. **What is the body's main source of energy?**

   Carbohydrate   Fat   Protein

2. **Soybeans and clover take away nitrogen from soil.**

   True   False

3. **Wheat was one of the first crops grown in the Middle East.**

   True   False

4. **Most farmers in the world practice this kind of farming.**

   Subsistence farming   Commercial farming

5. **Crops can be grown in desert regions.**

   True   False

6. **This is one of the oldest farm machines.**

   Grain drill

   Manure spreader

   Rotary hoe

7. **Rotary sprinklers are an example of this kind of irrigation.**

   Surface   Subsurface   Overhead

8. **Worldwide, which grain crop uses more land?**

   Rice   Corn

9. **Which is the larger type of cattle?**

   Beef cattle   Dairy cattle

10. **Commercially raised chickens lay about 300 eggs per year.**

    True   False